To DAWN
A special thank you from us all.

All best wishes
for your new life
& career in America
~ Amor.

GOOD LUCK
&
BEST WISHES
DANTE
NURSING OFFICE

All the Best.
We will miss you
with the P.P. Gs and
the Recovery Room.
6-5-97.

Good Luck + Best wishes
Agng.

Best luck + Best wishes Always

I Wish you good luck Irshad.

Wish you all the best.
Arou
6.5.97

Good luck and Best wishes.
I am sure when you will
see this book you will
remember all of us.
Ibrahim Salamma.

Best
Wishes
Always
Daphne

Ali

Dawn,
Good luck!
Jhai

Wish you All the Best

The OASIS

Gertrude Dyck *[signature: Gertrude Dyck]*

عزيزي دو كت
جدا بالرغم من معرفتنا القصيرة
في قيل عمساً أي العمل
والموضوع في أن أم لك بالسعادة
خالد واعتبرو
خالد
Khaled Al-Assand

Al Ain memoirs
of 'Doctora Latifa'

Published with the support
and encouragement of

AL SALAMI GROUP
AL AIN

MOTIVATE
PUBLISHING

DEDICATION

To all 'my children' —
the children born at Oasis Hospital,
and their children and the young men
and women of this generation, who
inherit a legacy of change and progress
and the responsibility to uphold the
standards and fulfil the dream that
HH Sheikh Zayed bin Sultan Al Nahyan
had for Al Ain and the Emirates.

Motivate Publishing

Dubai: PO Box 2331, Dubai, UAE

Abu Dhabi: PO Box 43072, Abu Dhabi, UAE

London: London House, 26/40 Kensington
High Street, London W8 4PF

Published by Motivate Publishing

First published 1995

ISBN 1 873544 90 1

British Library Cataloguing-in-Publication Data.
A catalogue record for this book is available
from the British Library.

Printed by Emirates Printing Press, Dubai

Village women carrying water in cooking pots make their way down a lane between date palm gardens, 1975.

*The roller-coaster desert track leading to Jebel Hafit, 1964.
The Chevrolet was sometimes used to transport patients of
the new Oasis Hospital, whose female staff adopted a
uniform of dress and surwal trousers.*

CONTENTS

FOREWORD

I am pleased to commend Dr Latifa for her dedication and insight in putting together this informative book. Her literary account and pictorial selection will undoubtedly be appreciated by the people of Al Ain and the UAE, especially those associated with the Oasis Hospital. Proper medical care is a key component in our country's quest to ensure a high standard of living. In chronicling the events surrounding the Oasis Hospital, Dr Latifa has made an important contribution of interest to both the medical community and those concerned with the development of the country.

In addition to enriching our impressions about Al Ain and its past, the establishment of the Oasis Hospital marks the beginning of the relationship between the UAE and the USA. Granted the right and full support of HH Sheikh Zayed bin Sultan Al Nahyan, Dr Pat Kennedy and his wife Dr Marian Kennedy embarked on their humane venture in 1960 in order to bring modern medical care to this area.

The Oasis Hospital is a glowing testament to the rapid progress the UAE has achieved. The Garden City of the Gulf, Al Ain has been blessed with a wonderful medical facility whose benefit will be enjoyed for years to come. I would like to thank the author for her unwavering effort in bringing this work to fruition.

Mohammed bin Zayed Al Nahyan

Driver and guide pause on a dune near Al Ain, 1964.

Faces of the future, 1971. The tradition of hospitality was ingrained in children from an early age.

Top right: View of Jebel Hafit from a mud-block building in Buraimi, 1963.

Bottom right: Newborn twins leave Oasis Hospital, 1964.

ON THE THRESHOLD OF CHANGE

THE OASIS CITY OF AL AIN lies about 160 kilometres east of Abu Dhabi, the capital of the United Arab Emirates. Known thousands of years ago for its strategic position and good water supply, Al Ain is still a vital link between the Indian Ocean and the Arabian Gulf — only today cars, trucks and planes have replaced the traditional mode of travel, the camel and donkey.

Perhaps nowhere else in the world has there been such a rapid and dramatic change in a country as there has been in the United Arab Emirates, where as much change has taken place in the space of twenty-five to thirty years as would have happened over a hundred years in many other parts of the world.

Of pure Bedouin stock, its people were strong and brave, inured of life's harshest elements of heat and scarcity of water, with a very limited source of income. Their hardship was compounded by the worldwide depression of the 1930s, together with the loss of their basic income from the pearl trade in the face of Japan's cultured pearl industry. With all this plus the rationing of the Second World War, they were at their lowest ebb. But even so, they were miraculously on the verge of beginning their greatest era — the era of oil.

For it was in 1939 that the first oil concessions were signed; in 1949 the first exploratory well was sunk; in 1959 was the first promising sign of oil, and on December 14, 1963 an oil tanker took on the first load of crude oil at Jebel Dhanna. The progress that followed was explosive: roads, schools, government housing for nationals,

Right: Homes built of mud bricks and palm branches border irrigated fields, with Jebel Hafit and its spur in the background, 1960.

Below: Al Ain of today is a blaze of colour and greenery in residential as well as garden areas.

modern hospitals and more were built at a breath-taking rate as Sheikh Zayed put his ideas for modernisation into practice.

Theirs was a quick transition from camels to Cadillacs, from shifting desert trails to six-lane highways, from little *'arish* huts to huge modern villas, from a meagre post-pearling income to a wealthy oil income: a wonderful transformation, almost overnight. It was a seemingly impossible task to produce modern thriving cities from virtually nothing, and to transform the desert into a haven of green.

I am very privileged to have witnessed this change first-hand; to have 'grown up' with the people of Al Ain in the United Arab Emirates. Even though there has been unprecedented rapid change in the physical make-up of the country,

yet the people have remained warm, kind and undaunted, and the average national is tenaciously hanging on to his age-old values and virtues.

I feel a tremendous bond, having also experienced a little of the harsh existence that they knew, and to have been with them through their growing pains. I learned to know and value the country by getting to know the people personally, experiencing their hospitality, their vivacious spontaneity. I learned of their rich heritage — a heritage of culture, of strength and perseverance — which sustained them when all the odds were against them. This can never be erased from anyone born in this land.

Development brings comforts and facilities that can be appreciated by people from all over the

world, but invariably also creates barriers to the kind of closeness I experienced more than thirty years ago. It is easy to romanticise the 'old days' when life really was appallingly hard. But the very struggle to survive creates a bond between people, one that transcends race or creed.

I hope my pictures and memories will help others feel the excitement, the thrill, the joy there was in knowing the people and the country in its unsophisticated form.

Much of my story is also the story of Oasis Hospital. Like the people it was created to serve, the hospital was caught up in the whirlwind of change. Inextricably bonded to the community, its development parallels that of Al Ain; its achievements are those of the people of the Emirates.

Local people welcomed the hospital and its staff; invitations to visit them in nearby and far-off villages followed. We would always be received with open arms, met at the car and accompanied on foot to their homes, be they in a date garden or beside the next dune. Their friendship was overwhelming. If they had given birth at the hospital, they would say: "You must come and see 'your baby'," as one is often honoured as the 'mother' when one cuts the cord of that baby at birth.

Today, Al Ain blossoms proudly as the Oasis City of the Gulf. It is a verdant carpet of life and vitality, green far beyond the original oases into what only a few years ago was barren desert. It is a tribute to its people and their leaders, above all Sheikh Zayed bin Sultan Al Nahyan.

Coming by camel to Al Ain for treatment, 1967.

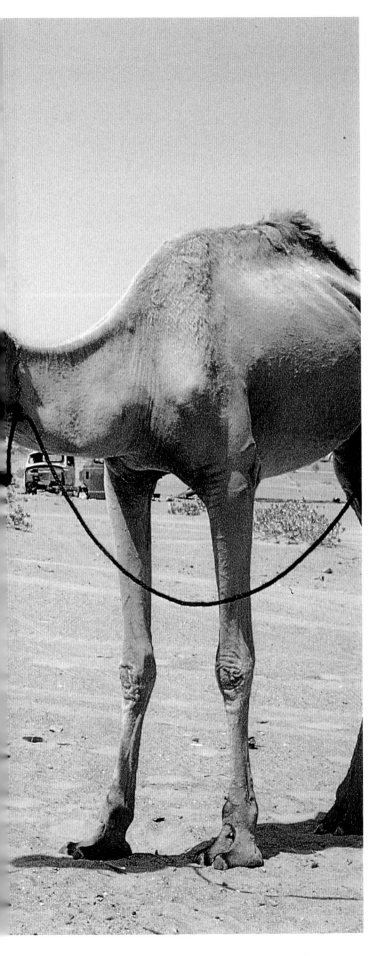

FROM SNOW DRIFTS TO SAND DUNES

COMING FROM THE WIDE-OPEN spaces of the Canadian prairies, I found the sands and plains of Abu Dhabi almost familiar, except that I was used to snow drifts in the winter and here there were sand dunes instead; and of course there was a vast difference in the temperature. Upon my arrival here, I realised that Arabia was not just all sand: it was made up of beautiful oases as well, such as the oasis of Al Ain to which I had come.

In 1960, while in my last year of training as a nurse, I applied through an international organisation for a position in the Middle East. Shortly thereafter, a letter came telling me of a doctor couple presently entering the 'Trucial Oman Coast' to start a hospital. They would need nurses. Would I be willing to go there?

Soon after that, I met Raymond Joyce who had been to Al Ain with Dr Pat Kennedy in 1959 and 1960, to meet Sheikh Zayed and his brother Sheikh Shakhbut who was the Ruler of Abu Dhabi at the time, and to decide on a site for the new hospital. I was bursting with questions. Later, when I saw his pictures of the enchanting desert sands, and of Al Ain where the hospital would be built, nothing could hold me back. I wanted to leave right away, but I realised I would need some practical nursing experience first. So it was not until December of 1962 that I was ready to leave my homeland and venture out to fulfil my life-long aspirations.

After hearing about the Trucial Oman States, as the area was known prior to the withdrawal of the British in 1971, I was advised to read Wilfred

Thesiger's book *Arabian Sands*. I was enthralled by his accounts of travelling in the desert. The chapter on the Buraimi Oasis was my main interest; to think that the hospital I was going to join was being opened there. Thesiger's stories of the Bedouin filled me with admiration: such stalwart, friendly people. I wondered what the women would be like. I even made a black veil with eye holes in it, to resemble the ones I saw in his pictures, to try to understand the women before I left home and to show friends what I thought they'd look like.

My father was apprehensive, and it was difficult for him to let me go so far away by myself — you needed a magnifying glass to find the Trucial Oman States on the world map — but letters from the staff here assured him that they would take care of me, and so he relented.

ON DECEMBER 17, 1962, I ARRIVED at Bahrain airport — the only international air access to the UAE at that time — with Edith Patterson, another Canadian, on the plane from Beirut. Raymond Joyce and his wife, who were now living in Al Ain, came to Bahrain to meet us, as well as their son who was coming from school in India.

When we landed in Bahrain, I was still wearing my heavy Canadian winter clothes: two sweaters, a heavy coat and winter overshoes. Was it hot! The others thought that it was beautifully cool. I quickly realised that I needed to pull out a cotton dress from my over-stuffed luggage, and then go to the *souq* to buy some light sandals. We went to the British Embassy while there in Bahrain, as well, to get a visa for my return to Bahrain for Arabic studies.

That afternoon we took a Gulf Air twin-propeller plane to Dubai, via Doha, Qatar. We stayed in the Trucial Oman Scouts' Guest House in Sharjah overnight, for the trip to Al Ain would take a full day. While in Dubai, we went to the old covered *souq* and then were rowed in the little wooden *'abra* across the Creek to the market on the other side. I could not believe that in the middle of December I could be sitting in a boat wearing a cotton dress with the warm breezes blowing over us from the Creek. I had just left Canada in sub-zero stormy weather. This was my first trip out of North America.

We set out the next day, on our eight-hour Land Rover ride to Al Ain. A local driver took us in his four-wheel drive in order to ford the sand

Above: Boys on their way to a celebration, 1963.

Left (from top): The author's first steps in
Arabia, 1962 — crossing Dubai Creek by 'abra;
at the entrance to Dubai airport; with her feet
in the sand en route to Al Ain.

dunes. We attempted to ascend some dunes several times before we could reach the top. Clouds of sand swirled up from the tyres as they churned through the sand; and of course a lot of it came in under the open back canvas covering and stuck to our faces and blew into our eyes! Nevertheless, I was thrilled to see the big sand dunes, and to get my first pictures of camels as we stopped and took off our sandals and walked in the warm soft sand. That was when I first got 'sand between my toes'. They say that when you once get sand between your toes, you can never get it out. The die was cast — I was destined to a wonderful, happy lifetime in the oasis of Al Ain.

From the last high dune, we sighted Jebel Hafit, the landmark of Al Ain, and the dark green of the palm groves in the distance. My school-book image of an oasis was of one palm tree beside a little pool of water. But here I found that the whole area was an oasis, with water supplied by *falaj*, underground and surface aqueducts, which brought the water from the Omani Hajar mountains to the plains. This was the life-line of the oasis, supplying water for man and beast to drink and to irrigate their palm groves.

I had expected to live in a desert tent, as depicted in Thesiger's book. When we arrived in Al Ain I was surprised to find that we had a nice mud-block building near the *souq* and also newly-built pre-fabricated houses at the new hospital site. We had running water from a nearby well, with flush toilets operated from a tank overhead filled by a hand pump. We also had our own six-kilowatt generator for electricity. Ours was one of only a very few homes to have such modern amenities because it had been used as Sheikh Zayed's Guest House for foreign dignitaries. When we finally arrived, we were received with big 'bear hugs' from the waiting hospital staff.

IN AL AIN, I FOUND THAT I WAS the first member of staff to come fresh to this hospital; the others had come from other Middle Eastern countries and spoke Arabic. When we went to visit local friends, they proceeded to talk to me and I was able to respond only with a smile or a nod, hopefully at the right time. Someone remarked to my colleagues, "She is so old and she doesn't know how to talk?" Most of them, at that time, had no idea that there were languages other than Arabic in the rest of the world. Those who arrived in 1960 were the first Caucasian

Right: 'Traffic' passing Oasis Hospital staff housing, 1963.

Main picture: Al Ain market and minaret under construction viewed from original Oasis Hospital site, 1963; (inset left) the Clock Tower roundabout is the focal point of the same area today.

women that had ever been seen here. They had never before seen women without masks and veils.

Back in Bahrain in January 1963 for Arabic studies, the American Mission Hospital who were to keep a watchful eye over me quickly searched for a teacher. They found a young local girl who had been to Beirut College for Women, and knew some English, and therefore was qualified to teach me Arabic. I soon found out that she was more interested in learning English than teaching me Arabic. I'd greet her with "*Sabaah el khair*" in my best practised Arabic, and she'd reply, "Good morning". I went to her home every day, but soon she was never there when I came. The family gave various excuses, though I couldn't really understand what they said. So I asked the American Hospital staff member who was assigned to supervise my studies to go and see the family. She came back and told me that the young girl had got a job, and that she was no longer available to teach me. But the family, in order to save face, just kept telling me that she was out, or not well, instead of telling me that she couldn't teach me any more. It was an introduction to Arabic cultural orientation; I realised then that I would have to make a lot of adjustments.

I had four months of study in '63, followed by practical use of Arabic by working at the hospital for a year and a half, and then had another 10 months of study from the autumn of '64 to the summer of '65. Arabic is a difficult language to learn, and there's no way to get the better of it except by diligent perseverance. But it is also a beautiful language: I love teaching it now to the hospital staff.

These have been happy years for me. I have never regretted coming to Al Ain: living here is like being part of a big family. Every day I learn something new from my friends as I listen to the stories of how they lived not so many years ago, and of their present-day gratefulness for the abundance that transformed their lives.

Bedouin water their camel, 1964. Loads of firewood lie about near the well.

Dr Pat Kennedy treats a patient in the courtyard of the old compound, 1961.

OASIS OF HEALTH AND PROSPERITY

THE ADVENT OF MEDICAL WORK was perhaps as crucial and historically life-changing for the people of Al Ain as was the discovery and exportation of oil to the whole of the UAE. Wealth without health, *maa fee fayada* — is useless.

Until 1960, there was no hospital as such in the Emirate of Abu Dhabi. There was the Maktoum Hospital in Dubai in the '50s and the Sarah Hosman Hospital which was mainly a maternity hospital in Sharjah, and a small maternity ward in Ras Al Khaimah. Dr MacAuley from the Maktoum Hospital would go to Abu Dhabi occasionally to see a few patients. The Rashid Hospital in Dubai was opened in 1973.

Upon the invitation of Sheikh Zayed and Sheikh Shakhbut, Oasis Hospital was opened in Al Ain in November of 1960. The hospitals which followed — Al Ain Hospital, opened in 1968, and Tawam Hospital which began in 1971 — all supplemented and substantiated that same concern and care for the people of Al Ain. What a thrill in 1994 to see the first graduation of medical students from the Al Ain University and to see the first Nursing School opened here in Al Ain in September 1993.

Dr George Mathews, the Medical Director of the Al Ain and Tawam hospitals, and Hilwa Balbakey, a nurse — two of the pioneers of the Al Ain Hospital — were still here after more than 25 years.

In the mid-1950s an Iranian couple, Thabit Mohammed Abdulla and Maliha Abaas Ismail, came to Al Ain, and contributed much to the health care of the people. He was a pharmacist and she was a midwife. Maliha performed home deliveries and sought to teach the people some health precautions, and Thabit ran a small compounder's shop in Al Ain. They also were still here well into the 1990s.

SHEIKH ZAYED AND SHEIKH SHAKHBUT, recognising the need for a hospital in Al Ain, decided to ask the hospital in Muscat to send them a resident doctor as they had been impressed with the American hospitals which they had seen in Muscat and Bahrain.

Dr Thoms, the head doctor in Muscat, said they could not supply a doctor, but that he knew of an American doctor who had been working in Iraq before the revolution there in 1958, and presently was working in Jordan, who he thought would be free to come. After contacting Dr Kennedy and arranging a visit for him, Dr Thoms came to Al Ain to introduce Dr Kennedy and Raymond Joyce who came with him, to Sheikhs Zayed and Shakhbut. That was in December of 1959. A subsequent visit was arranged for them the next spring, to choose a site for the hospital and to make the necessary arrangements for Dr Kennedy to bring his wife, also a doctor, and family and supplies, to make preparations for a hospital.

It was on their second visit in April of 1960 that Dr Kennedy had an opportunity to demonstrate his medical expertise, by assisting in the delivery of a VIP baby. The *Shyuukh* (royal family) were so pleased with Dr Kennedy's competence, and his pleasant and calm professional manner, that they eagerly awaited his return with his wife.

So on November 20, 1960, the first medical team arrived in Al Ain: Doctors Pat and Marian Kennedy, their four children and Maria Mayer. Within the first year though, nine other Western staff members joined them, plus Suleiman, an Arab clinic helper, his cousin Saleh, grounds manager, and Aslam, a Pakistani cook-cum-houseboy who is still on staff in the maintenance department.

The Guest House in 'downtown' Al Ain, near the present-day clock tower, had been designated as temporary quarters until the hospital and residences could be built on the chosen site in the Mutawa district.

Right: The Al Maktoum Hospital in Dubai, 1961.

Left: Sheikh Zayed at the well in front of the site for Oasis Hospital, 1960.

Below: The same well, 1963. The proximity of water was a deciding factor in choice of the site. Unfortunately, the well dried up within two years.

THE GUEST HOUSE WAS a mud-block compound; the rooms all around becoming part of the wall which encompassed the compound, were used as living quarters, including a communal living room, dining room and kitchen. A central building, originally a kitchen in the Guest House, was used as a clinic. A palm-stick awning was built to shade patients as they waited their turn to see the doctor.

One corner of rooms was designated as Labour/Delivery Room, an Operating Room, Sterilising Room, Storage Room and also a large VIP patients room with its own outside door and palm branch entrance courtyard. The patients' rooms (four of them) were built of palm branches just outside the wall beside the delivery room unit. It was very compact and efficient. And the patients were very happy with the arrangement. From the beginning, we had a separate room for each patient, so that their menfolk and family could visit them in privacy. There was a small communal courtyard, where they could make their coffee and visit together.

The Cosely pre-fabricated clinic building and the first three residences there were ready for occupancy by April of 1963.

The first maternity patient came on November 22, when the Kennedys hadn't even unpacked, let alone received all their supplies. But it was an uncomplicated delivery, and Dr Marian delivered her and took the mother and her new baby boy home in the hospital Land Rover, a few hours later. They named the baby Mubarak, which means 'the blessed'. She was the 'ice breaker' and the word spread like wildfire, to all the villages, near and far.

PATIENTS BEGAN TO COME to Oasis Hospital from Al Ain and Oman, seemingly from nowhere, to see the doctors and try out their medicine. The *ibra* or injection soon became a cure-all. Many came by camel, after many days of travelling, or by donkey; nearby villagers came on foot. Joyce Melhuish, acting as a receptionist/registrar in the clinic, likes to tell of the menfolk coming in there, and tapping her on the shoulder with their camel sticks, to get her to attend to them first, or demand that they be seen by the doctor, immediately. They always seemed to be in a hurry because they said their camels were waiting for them.

THE HOSPITAL BECAME THE CENTRE of social life, as well as the people's sole source of medical treatment. There soon were more than 200 patients a morning coming to the clinics. By the end of the second month, 1,000 patients were registered in the out-patient clinic. By the end of the fifth year, that number had grown to 20,000.

I remember a lady coming to the clinic nearly every day without any apparent illness, and I complained to Dr Marian, "Why does this woman come day after day and take up our time when she's not even sick, and so many who are really ill are waiting their turn?" Dr Marian answered softly, "Leave her alone. She won't take much time. She just wants to come to see us and all of her friends." She would get a ride with every car coming from their village that was bringing patients to the hospital. This was her outing for the day.

And of course, the maternity rooms were a hive of activity and excitement, as people came to visit and offer *baraka* or blessings for the new arrival. There were no specific visiting hours; they could come any time round the clock. And then, as now, family members would bring food to the hospital for patients.

Doctors Pat and Marian Kennedy left the hospital in June 1975, and were succeeded by the present medical director, Dr Larry Liddle. Known locally as Dr Fwad, he and his wife Marilyn (Layla) and their two children first came to the Oasis Hospital in October 1975.

Patients queue at the door to the registry, located in the
former kitchen of the Guest House, 1963.

MANY PATIENTS DID NOT HAVE MONEY to pay for their medicines and hospital care, so Sheikh Zayed and Sheikh Shakhbut issued nationals with a *burwa* so they could get treatment. They would arrive at the hospital with this little slip of paper rolled up in a ball and tied in a corner of the woman's *shayleh* or veil, or in the man's turban called a *sufra*, with the message to treat the patient on the Sheikhs' account and his signet ring seal on it. Occasionally a Bedouin would arrive without a *burwa*, and claim that he had no money, but when told that he couldn't get his medicine until he produced one or the other, he often would produce a Rs100 note from his turban, or from behind the *khanjar* or dagger on the belt. In those days Rs100, was a lot of money. The currency then was the Indian rupee. Maria Theresa dollars also was legal tender in the early 1960s. We used to get them quite frequently. I know, as I often had to work as cashier/pharmacist as well.

The practice of *burwas* was stopped when the Government hospital opened in 1968, first in Muwaiji and then later, in Jimi. The Government hospital was funded by the Ruler, and treatment was free. It then became a matter of pride for people to be able to pay for their own medicine.

A piece of paper with a number on it was something new to the people. So when they were given their clinic 'chittee', they would tie it in one corner of the *shayleh* or put it in the pocket of their dress or *condora*, and forget about it until the next time they needed it. Consequently, by then it would have been dipped into the *falaj*, or washed with the dress — occasionally even eaten by a goat. The stories about what happened to these humble chittees were guaranteed to have visitors in stitches of laughter.

Frequently, a villager would loan his or her chittee to someone who didn't have one. All would go well until the doctor asked about the previous illness, or the baby that was delivered just a month ago. Then things just wouldn't add up, and the patient would have to go back to the registry and wait to get his own card — like he should have done in the beginning.

*Above: The young Sheikh Khalifa bin Mohammed bin
Khalid Al Nahyan and his attendant, 1971.*

*Top left: A visitor with the omnipresent coffee pot in the
hallway of the Maternity Ward, 1963.*

Middle left: Joyce Melhuish greets patients, 1961.

Bottom left: An Arab family leaving the hospital, 1964.

IN FEBRUARY AND MARCH OF 1963, some fairly heavy rains caused much damage to the mud-block 'old compound'. Normally mud-block buildings could withstand light rain. They were coated on the outside with *juss,* a kind of baked lime, smeared on like stucco. This hardened but would also crack and chip off, exposing the mud bricks, if not maintained constantly. After seven years without rain, the sun and wind had taken their toll on many buildings, and although the Guest House was in reasonable repair, the heavy rain that year simply washed away corners of rooms, leaving them open to the outside world. This damage gave new urgency to the hospital's imminent move to the new site of pre-fabricated buildings.

At the new site, workmen had built eight rooms for patients out of palm branches with a courtyard in the middle — four rooms on each side. There was a water tap in the middle of the courtyard and a bathroom off the far end. The roof was made of corrugated aluminium sheets, and the doors were of Indian rug hangings. Some of the patients liked this cosy arrangement, for they could talk to each other through the walls, or ask if their neighbour had some bread, or the like. With the leafy part of the branches to the inside, we had hoped it would be 'peek-proof', although I can imagine that many a curiosity was assuaged by poking a hole where needed.

Patients' questions are fielded by Mona Joyce, who worked as administrative assistant, 1964.

I HAD BEEN IN THE GULF for nearly a year and I thought I knew quite a bit of Arabic. I soon learnt otherwise.

The women in the hospital were told not to cook inside the rooms, because the palm branches from which the walls were made still had the dried leaves on them, on the inside, and they could catch fire very easily. They could cook in the courtyard. However, one day, a lady decided to put her primus stove in the room because it was too windy outside. And the inevitable did happen. The primus stove must have given out a couple of bursts of flame that hit the wall, and in seconds, the room was ablaze.

I was in the next room bathing a baby, at about 5pm, and the lady from the next room came to me and said, *"Dow, dow."* I had learned that word as meaning light, so I wasn't in any big hurry to see what she was talking about; maybe it was the sunset she was excited about. I would finish bathing the baby first. In a minute, she was back again obviously quite determined to get her message across to me, repeating *"Dow, dow!"* Whatever it meant, I'd better go and see what light she was talking about. I saw — it was fire. I immediately screamed, *"Hariiga!"* the word that I had learned for fire (something on fire). I left the frightened women to get out of the rooms by themselves while I ran to find someone to help put out the fire. When I came back the women were sitting up on a little dune away from the hospital, with their babies wrapped in their outer coats, called *'abayas*. All their personal possessions were in the rooms, even their money under the mattress (where valuables were always stored) with their clothing and all.

The men arrived to fight the fire, but it was too late for those four rooms. They were in flames and the aluminium roofing was melting like chocolate. They quickly proceeded to tear down the other four rooms so they wouldn't burn also. But mercifully the wind turned direction, and the fire never came that way.

To the local Arabs, the only light they knew was from a fire, as the fire provided them with the only light that they knew at night — be it a camp fire or even a lantern light. So the two words to them were synonymous. And even today they use the word *'dow'* for 'light' and for 'fire'.

The Kennedys had just that day arrived back from America.

Fire damage was limited to the one row of patient rooms by a fortuitous shifting of the wind, 1963.

SINCE THOSE PALM BRANCH ROOMS were destroyed by fire in October of 1963, the next job for the men was to rebuild the rooms, this time with mud blocks or *teen*. The mud blocks were made right there, as the soil was actually clay. They would build four rooms, with the hope of building with cement blocks in the near future.

The mason spent several days making these mud blocks by hand and left them to dry in the sun. But, alas, that night it rained. And lo and behold, the next day there was nothing left but mud pies and the prospect of starting again.

THE CEMENT BLOCK FACTORY in Al Ain, which opened in 1976, produces 12,000 blocks per day, but back in the 1960s we had to make our own blocks — in fact, our own block-making machine.

Leon Blosser and family arrived in Al Ain in January of 1964. His first assignment was to build the hospital rooms with cement blocks. There was no place you could buy them; in fact the bags of cement had to be brought from Dubai. No one had ever built with cement blocks in Al Ain before, and many came to watch what was being done. Leon made his own cement block machine, using an old truck chassis and standing it on end. He did some welding and… there it was.

They had to haul the gravel from the wadi and sand from the desert, and then make all the cement blocks by hand. And they managed to do it, too. Gerry Longjohn arrived toward the end of 1964, and he helped to finish those first 22 rooms. Gerry also built a *majlis* or meeting room for the hospital (later used as the pre-natal clinic), also the first cement block residences and the X-ray building, with the basement below, for cool storage of medicines.

One problem in the first in-patient rooms was that they were built on slightly lower ground than the surrounding area, and when it rained, the place flooded. After some heavy rains in December '64 to January '65, patients who were used to sleeping on the floor suddenly moved up and perched on their beds. The staff were all busy with brooms and rubber scrapers trying to get the water out. Whoever dreamed that there could be so much rain in the desert?

Top: Family of a patient inside the mud-block rooms of the hospital, 1964.

Above: Concrete block construction, 1964. The blocks with their distinctive round holes were made on site with a 'home-made' machine by Leon Blosser, seen in the picture wearing Arab head dress.

Above and left: Making mud bricks on site, 1963. Heavy rain overnight destroyed the previous day's work.

THE HOSPITAL HAD 20 ROOMS by 1965. The 'windows' were just shutters at floor level, and the doors were swinging doors. Thus the air could flow even at night when the coolers were off. However, the patients also moved their beds outside at night. It was often difficult to find patients at night to give them medicine or check them. Most often the father would sleep on the bed, and the mother on the floor with the other children beside the new baby's cradle. They were swinging cradles, so she could rock the baby with one foot. They often tied a strip of cloth to a corner of the cradle, and the other end to the mother's big toe — so that she could just move her foot and rock the baby. During the day, young children one or two years of age would also be tied to mother this way, or to the leg of the bed, so that no one would need to run after them.

'IF YOU CAN'T BEAT 'EM, join 'em...' In the early 1960s, the women all sewed their own *burqas* (face masks), and this material was impregnated with a blue indigo dye, called *neal*. That *neal* would come off onto their fingers when they sewed their *burqas*, and also come off on their faces in the heat with their perspiration, and thus also onto their hands as they would sweat purple. Everything they touched turned a purple-blue, too. Consequently, it was decided to paint the doors of the hospital a deep blue, so that the *neal* wouldn't show. The women would have this blue colour all over their clothes as well. Now they use masking tape on the back of their *burqas* so that the dye doesn't come off on their faces — only on to someone else's uncovered face when they kiss them.

Top: Women at blue-painted registry window, 1964.

Middle: Swinging cradle in a villager's home, 1970.

Bottom: Mother and baby soaked with perspiration, 1969.

Opposite: Patient from Oman, 1961.

FROM ITS HUMBLE BEGINNINGS, Oasis Hospital has developed and expanded to meet the growing needs of its community. The original palm branch and mud-brick buildings of the early 1960s and the 20 cement-block rooms added in 1964 were in keeping with the local standards of the day.

In the years that followed, the labour and delivery suite and the X-ray building were added, along with a basement for 'cold' storage of medicines. In 1972, another 10 patients' rooms, with private bath, were added. During this time, staff housing was also being built, but in the late 1970s and early '80s, the hospital experienced a push forward for bigger and better residences. Today, there are more than 125 members of staff, most of whom live on the hospital grounds.

In 1985, new in-patient rooms with the obstetric, surgical and paediatrics suites were started. These were completed and in use by 1990. Then at the end of 1993, the original cement-block rooms were demolished to make space for the new out-patient clinic, to open in early 1995.

Landscaping with grass, flowers and shrubs has replaced the former bare sands and *ghaff* trees which used to lure the Bedouin to camp there during extended treatments for tuberculosis, burns or eye problems.

But time waits for no man; as Al Ain evolves, so does its first hospital, keeping pace with the community just as it has done over the previous decades. Founded in a spirit of friendship and trust, Oasis Hospital looks forward to a long future of service.

Above: Patients departing from their camp site in front of the new Oasis Hospital, 1964. The 'arish rooms beside the main building were built as a VIP suite and later used as a staff residence. Right: Oasis Hospital, in full bloom, 1994.

Raymond Joyce greeting Bedouin with camel train passing Al Ain, 1963.

LIFE IN
OLD AL AIN

NO ONE SAUNTERING ALONG on his camel
on the way to Abu Dhabi, back in 1960, would
have dreamt that thirty years later they would be
making the same journey on a six-lane highway.
When the first cars came in to the Emirates, they
had to rough it in the desert as the camels did,
their tyres deflated so that they flattened like
camel's feet and skimmed along the sand.
Granted, there were fewer accidents with camels
than with cars.

Drivers tended to follow in someone else's
tracks. Tracks thus became well-established, but
were not up to heavy use, such as carrying oil
drilling equipment or building supplies that began
pouring into the country. The first asphalt road
from Abu Dhabi to Al Ain was completed in
about 1969. When I came back from leave in
Canada in September 1968, it was partly
completed, but the section through the big dunes
after Saad was not yet finished. I was travelling
from Abu Dhabi airport in a Mercedes taxi and it
got stuck there.

I had brought back a phonographic record,
carefully putting it in the bottom of my suitcase to
keep it flat. When we arrived in Al Ain, it had
warped from the heat in the boot of the car, so
that when we played it the phonograph needle
went up and down as though it were on a roller-
coaster.

The road from Al Ain to Dubai was
constructed in about 1976-77. I remember going
to Dubai in late 1975, rushing a baby to Rashid
Hospital in the middle of the night; the driver
raced with his Mercedes over the rough dirt trails
and made it there in less than two hours. I was
holding my breath all the way as I sat in the back
seat holding the baby, beside Dr Liddle; the father
was in the front seat. We were back in Al Ain by
5am. Normally we would have used the Abu
Dhabi-Dubai road which would take a minimum
of five hours.

In the early 1960s you could count on one
hand the number of cars in Al Ain — an old
friend recently recited from memory the names of
their owners. Most of the vehicles were Land
Rovers, except for the Sheikhs' cars.

Anyone with a car would provide a taxi
service for the whole of his area. In 1970, records
showed approximately 8,000 cars registered in all
of Abu Dhabi; five years later the number was
five times that many.

Top: Tracks in the sand, 1971. Within Al Ain you could pick and choose whichever trail seemed least treacherous — hitting the least desert bushes or the least soft sand.

Left: Traversing dunes on the way to Abu Dhabi, 1964.

Above: The six-lane highway to Dubai today.

THE BEDOUIN WOULD OFTEN SLEEP at the bottom of a sand dune, so that the sand would blow over, rather than on them. But with the introduction of motor vehicles, this became very dangerous. A car coming to the top of a dune usually had to come up with quite a speed in order to make it to the top and then he would 'sail' down. But he wouldn't see the people at the bottom of the dune until he got to the top of it, when the lights shone down on them. By then it was very difficult to redirect the car in the sand to avoid hitting them. It happened on occasion that people were run over that way.

In the village, the locals would sleep on the roof-top of their houses, if they had a mud-block house, or in the yard if it was a palm-stick house. Then they would usually build a platform, called a *manaama*, about a foot or two high, on which they would put their mattresses to avoid the snakes or scorpions on the ground. But the people out in the deserts just put their mats out on the sand and slept there. And nearly every night someone would come to the hospital with a scorpion sting, or even a snake bite.

In 1963, everyone slept outside. We'd pull the sheets over our heads to keep out the sand and the sand-flies. Our beds were right out in the open, as we had no wall around the hospital at that time. Before dawn the Bedouin would be on the move already, often going right past us with their camels and yapping dogs.

After electricity was installed in 1972, everyone started sleeping inside in the air-conditioning, except for the older generation who claimed it was healthier to sleep outside.

IN THE 1960s WHEN THERE WAS no electricity at night, the night air was deathly still. Any car that was heard, was no doubt, coming to the hospital — the tyres crunched on the gravel as they crossed the wadi, and their headlights cut through the night as there were no other lights in the area. When the Bedouin approached with their camels, the weary yet excited chattering of the women with them could be plainly heard.

Right: The 'extended care' department, about 1965. Many patients would come with their sleeping mats and lie down anywhere near the hospital, and thus stay for several days' treatment.

Below: Bedouin setting up camp on the hospital grounds, 1964.

THE HOSPITAL STAFF WERE INVITED to all of the local community functions — the most auspicious being that of wedding festivities, be it a Sheikh's family or a bedouin.

We were invited to Al Wougan out in the desert to a simple wedding in a tent. Though the facilities were limited, the traditions and customs must still be followed. Hospitality extended to a *majlis* under the trees where a traditional meal of rice and goat was served to the menfolk and later to the women.

The women gathered in the tent; and even in this limited space, as is customary according to Islamic dictates, the bride was kept in seclusion behind a blanket hung over a pole in one corner of the tent. Someone was putting henna on her hands and feet and braiding her hair with rose petals and *yas*, and applying oily perfumes to her clothes and body.

She would wear the traditional green *thob* and *condora*, and would be totally veiled when taken out to meet her husband for the first time.

Cases of fruit and other foodstuffs are piled up beside the tent, which were used to feed the guests for two days of festivities.

Above: Wedding celebration, 1968. The men would gather and be served in the shade of the Sumra, while the women went to view the trousseau — the gifts to the bride — in the tent.

Left: Cases of fruit to be served to the wedding guests.

AL AIN MARKET LOOKED A QUAINT affair in the early 1960s; small, mud-block buildings with open stalls covered by palm branches. These stalls sold coffee beans, rice, sugar, lentils, spices, perfumes, dried tobacco leaf, dried salted fish and various herbs known for their medicinal purposes. Everything was in open boxes or in hessian sacks. There was also a small variety of tinned fruits, like peaches, pineapples and pears, alongside locally-grown dates, and limes and mangoes. Thin muslin material was sold for dresses and some army surplus jackets for the men. Of course, there were all the camel strappings and supplies.

The pleasing aromas of the spices, perfumes and the pungent smell of salted fish were something you could never transport with you. You could tell about it, show pictures of it, but you never got the full effect unless you were there yourself to see it and smell it. That memory will always remain with me.

By 1964, a few other shops had opened. Iranian merchants brought in many other goods, such as fabrics and various household goods. In 1967, Andalus opened the first small supermarket in Al Ain, and in the 1970s there was a Spinneys and later Choithram's, Lal's and much later, the Prisunic and then the Co-op.

In the early 1970s, stores began opening everywhere, a process which continues today. Al Ain's four main streets are lined with stores, banks, travel agencies and various businesses. Al Ain purposely does not allow high-rise buildings as in Abu Dhabi and Dubai, in order to retain that small town, 'back home' feeling.

A modern animal market has been built, along with a fish market and several markets for locally-grown fresh vegetables and fruit. Near Al Ain, a vegetable-processing and canning factory makes use of the bumper production for local consumption as well as export. The Al Ain Dairy Farm, about 25 kilometres from Al Ain, provides fresh milk and milk products mainly for Al Ain and the Abu Dhabi Emirate.

Right: The souq and main street of Al Ain, 1960. The foreigner pictured is Dr Kennedy.
Top: The main shopping area, 1963.
Above: The new livestock market, popularly known as the camel market.

IN THE DESERT AND THE VILLAGES, everyone owned a few sheep and goats. And goats are notorious for eating everything in sight. They would come into the palm-stick house and take whatever they could on their way out.

On a visit to a village, one family recounted with much laughter how they had found themselves in a predicament. The baby was crying but they couldn't find the rubber teat for the bottle, to feed him. They soon realised that the goat had eaten it. With no 'corner store' or vehicle to go and fetch a replacement, and with a baby crying for food, the solution was to kill the goat and try to retrieve the teat. They did just that, and found it intact in the goat's stomach. They washed it well with soap and water and then fed the baby.

On another occasion, a woman described how she had come into the house and caught a goat eating a Rs100 note — she was just in time to see part of it sticking out of the goat's mouth — but by the time she had caught the goat, it had swallowed the money. A hundred rupees was a lot of money in those days. A man came that afternoon to buy a goat. "I'll sell you this one for Rs120," she said. She told him her plight. The buyer was sceptical, but when he slaughtered the goat, his wife found the money in the goat's stomach, undamaged.

The goats kept by Al Ain people would be taken out to the pastures daily for grazing. It was a communal system: one boy would go past all of the homes in the morning, and the goats would come out to follow him. At about 4pm they would come back again, and it was interesting to watch the goats racing to their own homes. They would 'knock' at the door, and the owner would let them in to the courtyard. The goat-herder was paid Rs5 a month by each owner.

Above: Wedding guests, 1974.

Top left: Two 'kids' on the outskirts of Al Ain, 1964.

*Left: Bedu in the desert with their herd of goats,
1971. Their tents were partly made of goat hair.*

DESERT FOLK COULD ALWAYS get along with
a minimum of equipment. After all, when you cart
all your earthly possessions on a camel's back,
you think twice as to whether you really need
something. And besides, since next to nothing
was available in the *souq,* you couldn't buy much
even if you wanted to.

Tribesmen and women were always camping
on the hospital grounds and cooking out in the
open. Hospital staff were often invited to have
coffee with them.

I remember one particular time when the man
of the household was the chef, and he baked
some bread for us. He had no oven, no bread
pans, no big mixing bowl. He didn't need them.
He mixed the flour, salt and water in a small bowl
with his fingers, and kneaded it a bit. Then he
pushed the coals of desert bush fire to one side,
made a flat cake of his dough and placed it on
the hot sand, where the fire had been, and then
put some of the coals on top of the dough. He
left it to bake for a few minutes and then took it
and brushed the sand from it and broke it into
pieces in the bowl. He poured a bit of water over
it to wash off some sand (for our sake, I
presume) and then poured some liquid butter on
it from a small kettle, and then some local honey
from a small bottle. He offered it to us with pride.
We admired what he had accomplished too and
of course, ate with him. It was quite tasty with the
butter and honey, and rather 'crunchy' with the
sand. We appreciated his hospitality. Custom
demands their best, and the local Arabs were
masters of this attribute.

Above left: Grinding wheat, 1974.
Left: Carrying home firewood, 1971.
Above: Baking bread required only the
bare essentials.

IN SEPTEMBER '63 THERE WAS A WEEK of
festivities and celebration in Al Ain near the
hospital. To the casual Western onlooker, it could
have been a wedding celebration, but why this
cluster of tents with one or two men going in and
out? Were there several brides? No, the tents
contained 40 young boys, aged between six and
nine years old, who had all been circumcised.
They would stay in the tents until they were
healed and the celebrating was to congratulate
their initiation into full Islamic rites and
requirements, and to provide a diversion (by
hearing the dancing) to help them endure
the pain.

Because Sheikh Zayed's son was one of those
circumcised, people came to congratulate him,
and of course the Sheikh paid the bill for the
festivities, the food and all — which would
always attract the whole community.

There was dancing to the strains of a goatskin
bagpipe, a reed pipe, the local made small skin
hand drums and the big barrel drums played with
the slap of the full palm of the hand. The dances
were the usual dancing by the men in a circle
with their swords and guns, then the *ayaala*
where there are two rows of men who sing to
each other. Another dance is the mock sword
fight with the short straight daggers and the
wooden round shields. They attack the opponent
with a 'hop, skip and jump' and pretend to
'capture and kill' their victim.

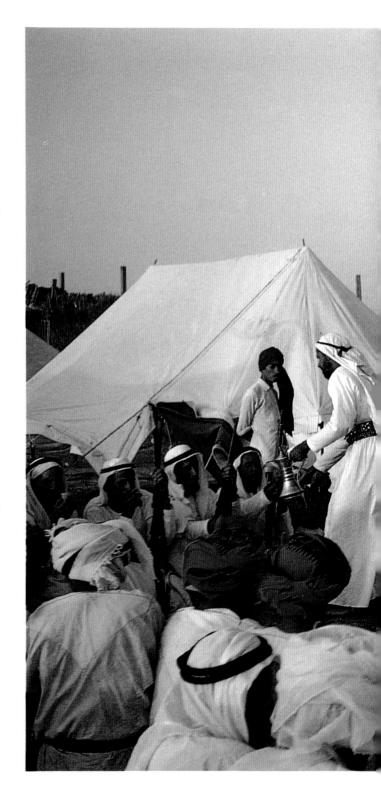

HH Sheikh Zayed, with Sheikh Shakhbut and Sheikh Mohammed bin Khalifa on his right, observing the traditional dances, 1963.

Above: Celebration site with tents and cars flying the Abu Dhabi flag, 1963.

Above left: Women in their finery take part in some of the traditional dancing.

Above right: Mock sword fight.

Left: Traditional ayaala *dancing. In the foreground with sword stands the late Mohammed Sheybaan, a noted dancer.*

AL AIN'S POPULATION TODAY is estimated at 280,000. In the early 1960s the whole of the oasis (nine villages) was estimated to have approximately a population of 2,000. This number was augmented from the late 1950s and early 1960s by an influx of expatriates. They made contributions in many sectors, as indeed they were already doing on the coast, notably in agriculture.

Abdul Hafeez Khan was the first government employee to come here through the British Middle East Development Division, in Beirut. He had a degree in agriculture, and was employed by Sheikh Zayed through the Political Agency of Abu Dhabi to come to the 'Buraimi Oasis' to work directly under Sheikh Zayed, who was then the deputy ruler of Abu Dhabi, and the Ruler's representative in Al Ain. Khan arrived in September of 1962 and planned and supervised all the planting of trees and the roundabouts of Al Ain that we see in the early pictures. He and his wife Mahfouda are still in Al Ain and still live in the same house originally built for them, next to the British Embassy residence in Al Ain.

In the early 1960s, the British officers of the Trucial Oman Scouts and the bank managers of the Eastern Bank (now Standard Chartered) and the Ottoman Bank (now ANZ & Grindlays) were about the only Western people in Al Ain, besides those at the hospital. But starting around 1966, there was an ever-increasing influx of foreigners: the road construction, the General Electric power plant, building construction and various other jobs brought in new workers from Britain, Europe and America, as well as India, Pakistan and other countries of the Arab world. They came under the oil companies or construction companies. They were architects, engineers, agriculturists, executives, financiers and teachers: in short everyone needed to make Al Ain into a beautiful and modern 20th century city.

Above: 'Doctor, look at my sore!' An opportune moment for a private consultation with the doctor, 1966.

Right: Ain Al Fayda leisure area was developed at the site of an artesian well discovered in the early 1960s.

Far right: Landscaping in its infancy at the roundabout near the Grand Mosque, formerly called the guest house roundabout, 1968.

BEFORE THE ADVENT OF MAINS electricity, the hospital's small six-kilowatt Petter generator was not strong enough to run air-conditioners, so we brought in 'desert coolers' in about 1963. These were wonderful. They had a big barrel fan with pads on three sides over which water was run. The fan drew the air in through the wet pads and thus cooled the air. They did not work if it was humid — so they were well suited to Al Ain but not the coast. They were installed in the hospital in 1965-66, perhaps the first place in Al Ain to have any 'central' cooling.

There were never any windtowers in Al Ain. I heard the reason was that they worked better in humid conditions such as are found on the coast.

Mains electricity became available in Al Ain in stages. The first areas wired, in 1968-69, were downtown and the palaces; electrical power didn't reach the outlying areas until 1971-72. The first people who got electricity of course ended up sharing their TV and air-conditioning et cetera with their neighbours. It took a couple more years until there was enough power and enough lines to go around. People in the outlying villages were buying TVs that would run on batteries, and even electric lights to run on batteries (to 'keep up with the Joneses') until the power lines finally reached their homes as well.

Of course, when electricity was available, the market could not keep up with the demand for air-conditioners. Once we tasted the joy of a comfortable cool night's rest, and comfortable cool rooms during the day, no one could stop the drive to buy more air-conditioners until there was one in every room.

Then the market also profited from the need for fuzzy warm blankets and quilts to keep people warm when they slept, in the summer, with the ACs turned to the coldest settings.

Above: The hospital Buick outside the Eastern Bank in Al Ain, 1966. The bank later became the Standard Chartered Bank whose building (inset) is a modern landmark in Al Ain's business district.

Right: A 'desert cooler' attached to the author's house, 1965.

THE MOST AMAZING THING was how fast news would get around with no telephones and no newspaper. The communication centre was the *falaj* where the women went every day, several times a day, to get their water. This was the place to exchange all the village news, plus updates on current events.

The women would carry heavy containers of water on their heads, with another – or a baby – in their arms, walking for many miles. No wonder they had such beautiful posture.

The menfolk always sat together sipping their coffee, eating dates and exchanging the news of the latest happenings in the village or between the tribes. They greeted each other with the question : *"Shu akhbarak?"* (What's your news?) Whether in the home or out in the desert, they would sit and discuss the recent political and social happenings. Whether on camel or in a Land Rover, they would always stop and ask about the 'news'. Even today, Arabs will greet each other with *"Shu akhbarak?"* just as Westerners would say, "What's new?"

I didn't see any phones at all in the Emirates when I came, at the end of 1962. If anyone wanted to get a message through to the 'outside world', they would go to the TOS or the British Agencies who had 'cable and wireless'. Sometimes you could feel pretty isolated.

The local telephones with international hook-up were not installed until 1970. All of the UAE had about 9,000 telephones in 1971. Today there are estimated to be more than half a million telephone subscribers in the UAE.

Mail in the 1960s came to Dubai, c/o the Trucial Oman Scouts, who would fetch it to us whenever they made a trip to Dubai, about once a fortnight. The first Al Ain Post Office was opened in 1968, in a small palm-branch building. The move to the present Post Office was in 1972.

Top and above: The falaj *was not just a place to wash and collect water, but an important village meeting point to exchange news. 1971, 1976.*

Right: Carrying heavy containers of water on the head, with another under an arm, was a skilful balancing act, 1971.

WHERE AND HOW PEOPLE LIVE certainly is a reflection of their income but more so, their character. The Arabs are a proud people, with dignity, demanding honour and respect. This was evident in their dwellings, progressing from *bait sha'ar* — Bedouin tent — palm-stick house or mud-block house to their free government housing, and now to their present-day modern villas.

Traditionally people built their own homes, working with their extended family, and with the servants of the household, in the case of the wealthier families.

The first mud-block buildings were built on a relay system. The workers were lined up at intervals from the clay mixer to the building, and the bucket of clay and the blocks would be passed on from one to the other, shouting, singing and laughing. It took a bit longer, but it got done — they knew no other way, and it had an element of fun in it.

Their homes showed their character. A simple tent or palm stick home would be neat and clean, with the trays and pots and pans scrubbed and out in the sun for sterilising. In the desert, they seldom had water to wash their trays, and the pots got very sooty from the fire so they were cleaned with sand.

With no-one but themselves to do the work, they took it all in their stride, remaining cheerful and jolly. There were many women working together, as they lived in extended family groups. Those times remain precious memories for the older generation. They remember having to crowd very closely together around a tray to eat their main meal, and they had to eat quickly, as there were always more people waiting to eat, and the poor of the neighbourhood would get what was left over. Nothing was wasted.

INTERESTING BALUCHI ROUND HUTS dotted the countryside as the labour force expanded. These igloo-shaped dwellings were built from a palm branch frame, and covered with anything that was available, most often with palm-leaf woven mats, but also sometimes cardboard or aluminium sheeting. When the Oasis Hospital moved to its present site, a Baluchi family working for the hospital moved over and set up house, along with all their relatives. Soon a whole colony was living behind the hospital. When the Government housing scheme took over that land, the Government also provided them with housing in other areas.

IN 1967, WHEN THE GOVERNMENT started providing free low-cost housing (with sewage disposal and running water) for the local Arabs, their life-styles began to change to a more indoor life. Many of the Bedouin, however, brought in from the deserts to these new cement homes, felt claustrophobic. So their doors would always be left open in spite of air-conditioning because they wanted to see the sands and their animals. That custom persists to this day; the people of Al Ain love to sit outside as soon as the weather is a little cooler, especially in the evenings.

Above right: An 'arish home in the village of Hafit, 1967.
Right: Building an 'arish, 1964.

A Baluchi house with a stone-marked mosque in the foreground, 1963. Fort Jahali can be seen on the horizon, a view which today is hidden by low-rise buildings and vegetation.

THE TRAILS OUT IN THE DESERT were a challenge to follow, as you never knew if you would find the same trail twice. The wind would blow and change the landscape, and cover your well-worn trail completely.

Night travel was particularly 'adventurous'. There were no landmarks, no street lights, and even the homes only had lantern light, but you couldn't see it shining through the palm-stick walls until you got very near to them. We often got lost, or hit the wrong trail that would take us to some wadi, or a big dune. We frequently got lost on the way to Zakhir, as it was all sand dunes, and we'd occasionally end up on the other side of Jebel Hafit.

Out in open dune country, as was the case on the road from Al Ain to Abu Dhabi, it could be disastrous, as one could easily get lost. At first we always went with local drivers, as they knew every inch of the trail: every sand dune, every tree. Each one was named, for they had travelled there for years by camel-back, or walking beside the camel. Later we became more confident about navigation, but desert travel still had its tense moments, at least for some. Others, like Gerry Longjohn, developed that sixth sense that the Bedouin had for finding the trail. One time when we nervously told Gerry that we were afraid he was lost, as there were no trails to be seen anywhere, he replied with a smile: "Oh yes there are — just look behind us."

IN THE 1960s EVERYONE had to check in at the police station in Al Ain before leaving for Abu Dhabi, and take a slip of paper from them to be presented at the police station at the Muqta crossing and also to the police in Abu Dhabi. Going back you had to do the same. In this way they had a record of all people travelling, and could send a search party out for them if they did not arrive in the specified time. Of course you never went anywhere without water for the Land Rover, as well as for drinking, and also extra petrol.

Above: Aerial view of the Sanaiya district, 1973. The dirt trail from the souq went past the hospital (foreground) and Al Ain Municipality buildings (middle ground) connecting with the trail going through the spur of Jebel Hafit, to go on to Muwafaga (now called Zakhir). About 1973 the bridge and road were put in past the hospital, on the left side, joining the Sanaiya Road. The road across the mountain with the bridge spanning the wadi there, going towards the Hilton Hotel, came later, about 1977-78. Inset: A view across Al Ain today.

THE TRUCIAL OMAN SCOUTS (TOS) were stationed in the Fort Jahili in Mutarad, just across the wadi from the hospital. There was nothing to be seen between Oasis Hospital and Fort Jahili; now it is in the park across from Sheikh Khalifa's Palace and can't be seen from the hospital at all.

The British TOS men were regular visitors, especially in the summer, the main drawing card being that we had kerosene refrigerators, which they didn't have. That meant a drink of cold water; otherwise it was luke-warm water all summer for them.

The TOS army rations included a lemonade mixture which they shared with us. But it was so potent that we nicknamed it 'Battery Acid'. However, they kept us well-stocked all summer, in exchange for the cold water. In the winter, their rations also contained chocolate bars, something we never could get in the early years. It was a real treat when they shared those with us too. The locals kept their water in clay pots, often with hessian sacking around them to keep the pots wet; the evaporation would cool the contents. Even today these pots can be seen hanging in many gardens, reminiscent of the past.

The TOS left in 1971 when the United Arab Emirates was formed. It was the end of an era. The British had contributed so much to the country, and many young local men who worked with them owed their education and their maturity to them.

Trucial Oman Scouts positioned at the causeway to Abu Dhabi, and (inset above) guarding the causeway entrance, 1961.

Right inset: TOS entering Fort Jahili in Al Ain, 1971.

THE TOS COULD SUPPLY a mercy flight, and would transport patients to Dubai or Bahrain during an emergency. They had a telegraph set-up, and so any emergency messages were sent through them too. Oasis Hospital, in return, gave the TOS free services: all the routine medical checkups and X-rays for their men, besides treating any illnesses.

Their army medic was also prepared to treat some of the local people out in the deserts or far-off villages. In fact he treated me on one occasion, when we had invited a couple of the men for Sunday dinner. I had opened, or was trying to open, a tin of butter (the butter was all canned); my thumb, greasy from the butter, slipped and was cut deeply from the sharp edge of the lid. The medic ran to his jeep and got a bandage, and secured it tightly around my thumb so that we could proceed with the meal. After dinner, I went over to the hospital and the doctor sutured it up.

WITH THE OPENING OF the Al Ain International Airport on March 31, 1994, there were six international airports in the UAE, a far cry from the 1960s, when the only international air access to the UAE was via Bahrain. From there you would take a small Gulf Air twin-engine 'shuttle service' plane, touching down in Doha, then on to Sharjah, Dubai or Abu Dhabi.

The Abu Dhabi Arrivals and Departures lounge was an open veranda on a mud-block building in the desert. The runway was packed *sabkha*. But they did serve cold drinks from a kerosene fridge.

Top right: Sheikh Zayed (second from right) in his majlis *in Al Ain. Those with him include (from left) Sheikh Maana bin Mohammed el Dhahiri, Major John Pott of the TOS, Sheikh Mohammed bin Khalifa Al Nahyan, and a judge from the Sharia Court.*

Top left: Sunset prayers on the open veranda of the 'Arrivals and Departures' lounge at Abu Dhabi Airport, 1963.

Right: An RAF plane providing emergency airlift to Dubai, 1964.

CAMEL'S MILK WAS ALWAYS a staple yet a speciality. It was an honour to be offered camel's milk. It always had some foam on top, as it came directly from the camel, and often was served in a large bowl which would be passed around for each to drink from. Even today when it is served in individual cups, each must have a bit of foam on it. It was always served fresh and warm, with sugar in it. People would buy big solid cones of sugar, called '*bluey*'; a piece was broken off and dipped in and out of the warm milk, until it was dissolved.

I never did like milk, so I usually refused the camel's milk too. But in the presence of Sheikh Zayed, when it was served at his palace in Al Ain, I didn't feel I had that prerogative. I tasted it... and enjoyed it, as it was piping hot and had sugar and cinnamon in it. It was really good.

A MUCH REPEATED STORY concerns the early years when there was no imported fresh fruit, when tinned fruit preserves were widely used instead. Nothing was wasted, so the juice that came with the preserves was always drained and passed around in a bowl for each to have a sip of it. A similar 'finger bowl' was also passed around, and of course the inevitable happened to my colleague Joyce Melhuish. When the bowl of fruit syrup was passed to her, she presumed it was the finger bowl and proceeded to dip her fingers into it, quickly discovering her mistake. However, the local friends were not as upset about it as she was. No problem — we drank it anyway.

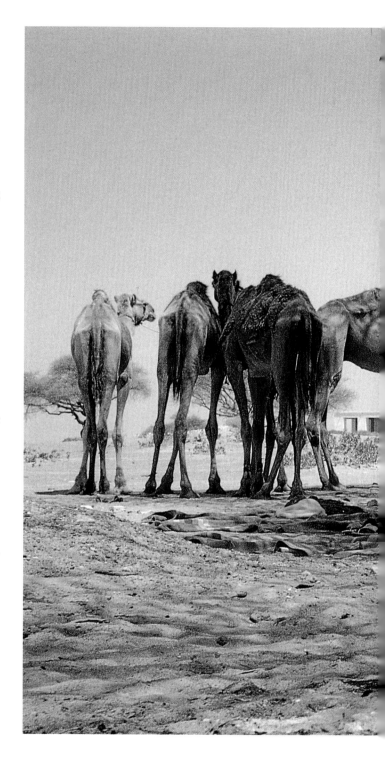

Omani village folk camp on the hospital grounds, 1967. With the camels resting and the goat-skin bags hanging in the trees, the well-used coffee pot takes its rightful position.

In early 1966, we were invited by Sheikh Said bin Shakhbut to visit the Liwa Oasis, the Nahyan ancestral home. Sheikh Said supplied two Land Rovers, with drivers and a guide as he said we wouldn't know the way, nor how to drive in the desert. We took along food and bedding to camp out for five days. I went with the Kennedys, their four children and Aslam, their cook. It was a memorable occasion indeed.

Our first stop was for lunch with a Bedouin family out in the sands about half-way to Tarif. They slaughtered a young goat and cooked the rice while we rested and cooled off in the shade of their tent, waiting for the meal. Then we went on and spent the night on the beach of Tarif. The next day the ride over the huge dunes of the Liwa was absolutely breathtaking. Our drivers knew how to drive along the crest of the dune and then find the right spot to go down. Many times we went up the steep side of the dunes and then drifted down the other side. Standing in the back of the open Land Rover, we got the full feeling of the ups and downs.

We stopped for the afternoon in the depths of the Liwa beside a very high dune with palm trees at its foot. We tried to climb the sand dune, and the children at least were successful. It was so high that a 45-gallon oil drum on its crest looked from below like a soft-drink can.

The sands were a beautiful red colour; the crests of the dunes were a deep red with larger grains of sand, almost like little beads. We gathered several samples, from the white sand on the beach of Tarif, to the brown and finally the golden colour of the dunes on the borders of the Empty Quarter.

Entering the Liwa area, we saw the flames of the gas flared off at the oil wells. What a strange sight in the midst of those mountainous barren sand dunes. This was not only the ancestral home of the Nahyan family, it was also the 'home', the source area of the wealth of Abu Dhabi. It meant progress and wealth for the people of the Emirate.

We saw the oasis, stopped at Mariya and Mariya Gharabiyya and other villages, and visited some of the local families, camping each night in the sands.

The trip to the Liwa today is a different story with the paved roads and hotels, but the sight of the dunes can still take my breath away.

Above: A driver washes his feet in preparation for his prayers, during the trip to Liwa, 1966. The Land Rovers carried all the supplies for the five-day trip across the sands.

Left: A desert encampment half way to Tarif, 1966.

WOMEN'S CLOTHING IN THOSE days varied quite a bit from that of the present day, not least in the fact that a woman's wardrobe was very limited. She didn't need a clothes closet with hangers; indeed, she had never seen nor heard of such luxuries. The couple of dresses that she owned were neatly folded and placed in a big wooden chest, or in a steel trunk, having been treated with perfume and incense.

The traditional Emirates dress is the *thowb wa condora*, the long loose dress with the thin sheer over-gown, the *thowb*. In the early times, the *thowb* always had a 'train' on it. The women became very adept at picking up that train between their toes, and then tossing it up over the arm. They could do this even while carrying something on their heads. They had the *khawaar* (embroidery stitching) or *telli* (the silver braid) on them, but not as heavy, nor as expensive as that of today.

The bridal dress traditionally was a green *thowb* and *condora*. Today they wear beautiful modern embroidered and beaded white wedding gowns, more beautiful than any that you will find in Western 'brides' books'.

Their dresses were usually made of thin cotton muslin brought in from India, or else from heavy embroidered silks. The *'abaya* or black coat was usually of loose weave wool with real gold braid around the front edge. The wool *'abaya* kept them warm in winter, but in the summer it was largely abandoned.

The dresses were always personally hand-tailored. Each woman knew her size: the length in so and so many *dhira'a* (cubits) which was the measurement of the forearm from the elbow to the tip of the second finger, and the waist and other measurements were by the measurement of a *shibar* (a handspan) from the tip of the thumb to the tip of the small finger. These measurements were quite accurate, the former being half a yard and the latter a quarter of a yard, or nine inches. They would take the thread from the material itself, where they had torn it (scissors were used only when there was any other than a straight line, like the slant of the sleeves) and this thread was used for stitching the dress by hand. Voilá, matching thread. The seams were rolled and hand-sewn so that they would not ravel, and the fabric, for stitching, was held tight by wrapping it around the big toe and stretching it to be held between the knees. Of course, they sat on the floor while sewing or cooking.

The *khawaar* (embroidery) was done by tailors in the market, but it would cost only two to five rupees. Today, it may cost up to five hundred dirhams. A bride's dress might cost thousands of dirhams. The stitching used to be in real silver and other colours as well. You knew it was real silver, for it tarnished. Of course it was not as wide and ornate as it is often today, but it was considered quite adequate and stylish. Most of the dresses wouldn't have any *khawaar* on them, as the women couldn't afford it, nor did they get to the *souq* that often.

The *surwalls* or long under-pants were also of fine cotton or pure silk. The *baadhala* or silver braid on the ankle of the pants, was made of pure silver strands with black and red threads. They were very expensive in those days, about fifty to sixty rupees, so only the wealthy women could afford it. It could be sewn on to the next new pair of pants, as it never wore out.

The women's jewellery was of solid twenty-two-carat gold: the Bedouin ladies used to sport solid silver. Usually, what a woman owned would be that which was given as part of her dowry. She would wear it any time she dressed up.

Top: The high standing of this Sheikh's wife from inner Oman can be seen in her many decorative rings and heavy gold neck jewellery, 1968.
Right: Weaving a goat's-hair rug, 1975.

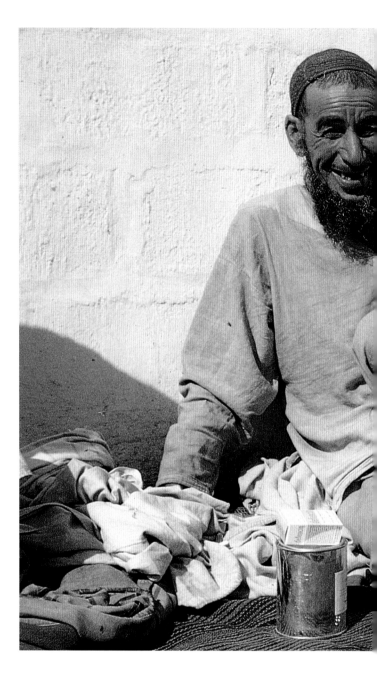

A WOMAN'S HAIR IS her crowning glory and beauty. It is worn open and loose to show the full beauty and length only at her wedding, but other than that it must be pinned up and covered. The Arabs usually have lovely thick black locks, which is made shiny and soft with the application of natural locally-grown henna.

In the 1960s, the women's hair was braided in small tight braids all around her head, and then those braids were braided together to make one large braid at the base of the skull. How it was braided together depended on what tribe she was from. But most women would weave nice smelling petals, like rose petals, *yas* etc. into the braids, as well as oil of *ambar* and *'aoud*, in order to exude a delightful smell. To top it all off, when the incense burner was offered it would be held under the braids to enhance the effect of the oily perfumes, as it does also in the clothes.

The Bedouin men also wore their hair long in those days, but it was always worn loose. They obviously did not have a barber's shop just over the next sand dune.

Above: Sitting outside the hospital with medicines, 1967. The girl's hair is ornately braided and decorated around her head.

Right: A classic woman's hair style of small tight braids all joining into one large braid at the base of the skull, 1968.

CHILDREN WERE INGENIOUS and creative in making their own toys. They probably valued them much more than the ones they buy from the toy shops today. Things as simple as marbles were very precious. You couldn't just go and buy some. Shopping trips to the coast were rare, and of course money was scarce.

A story has it that some children were playing with marbles while the baby was crawling around on the floor. The baby of course got three marbles, proceeded to put them in his mouth and swallowed them all. The older boy went crying to his mother; the baby had taken his marbles. "Well, where did he put them?" she asked. "He swallowed them," he wailed. His mother didn't believe him, but at the same time she was worried about her baby if he had swallowed these marbles. So they went to the '*musteshfa Kenned*' hospital for an X-ray, and sure enough, there were the three marbles all in a row, entering the small intestine. In two days' time, as the doctor predicted, the baby passed the marbles. So they washed them and brought them to show the doctor before giving them back to the older boy.

THE *FALAJ* PROVIDED SOME RELIEF from the heat when we would go 'swimming' (sitting) in it with our clothes on. There would always be a crowd of women and children watching; they'd all get out when we came. The 'pool' was about four feet by six feet and the water about eighteen inches deep. It was enclosed by a 'peek-a-boo' mud wall around it and a palm-branch roof for shade. But it served the purpose of allowing us to get wet and cool off. It was running water which would go to water the palms and other trees in the garden; but it had little fish in it that nibbled at your legs and feet, so you had to keep up a continual sort of dance to keep them away.

Many locals who had wells for their gardens would have their own *birka* which was a holding tank for the water. These, then, also became 'swimming pools' for the kids of the family. It was a special privilege to be invited to share their luxury.

Top: 'Swimming' in the falaj provided some respite from the heat, 1971.

Above: Falaj running through the date groves, 1967.

Right: Toy cars made from tins show a child's ingenuity, 1971.

THE FIRST MODERN SCHOOL in the Emirates opened in Sharjah in 1953 for boys aged six to seventeen, followed in the late '50s in Abu Dhabi, Dubai and Ras Al Khaimah. The first boys' school in Al Ain began in 1958; schools for girls came in 1967, and just 10 years later, in 1977, the Al Ain University opened with approximately 500 students the first year. What a feat: Only 25 years from the start of education until the establishing of a university.

A LOCAL LADY TOLD ME about her young son who wanted to go to school with his older brother. There were no birth certificates at that time, so no-one knew his exact age. So the teacher set the criterion for a boy's attending as having already lost his two front teeth.

This little boy didn't meet the qualification, and was upset about not being allowed to go to school with his brother. A few days later, he came home from play, face and clothes spattered in blood. Grinning proudly, he said, "See, Mom, now I can go to school." He had knocked out his own teeth with a rock. How could a teacher refuse such determination?

It was a proud little boy who took his place beside his brother, albeit only for a few days. He didn't actually start school until the next year, but when he did, he was first in his class all the way through school. He went on to university in the USA and today has a high position in the Municipality and Town Planning of Al Ain. His older brother is in Finance and Investment in Abu Dhabi and the younger brother is in the Ministry of Education in Al Ain.

Those boys had lost their father when they were very young and their mother brought them up alone. She tells of how the boys were so eager to learn that they would study late into the night by the light of a small kerosene lantern. Concerned about their eyesight, she tried to stop them from studying, but to no avail. So she went to Sheikh Tahnoun, and told him that her boys needed electric light so they could study at night. The next day, she said, a line was strung from the meagre street lights of Al Ain to her house; that night they had light from a single bulb dangling from the ceiling of their mud-brick home. Her boys would study.

Today, it is this lady's grandchildren from Abu Dhabi who live with her while they go to the Al Ain University.

*Above: The first Boys School, opened about 1958. The
barbed-wire fence was to keep the goats out, not the
children in.*

Left: Some of the pupils, 1963.

SHEIKH ZAYED HAS LONG HARBOURED a vision of Al Ain as a haven of green for his people. In fact he alerted archaeologists to his belief that there had been a river in Al Ain thousands of years ago. Experts say he may be right.

During the reign of Sheikh Zayed the Great (1855-1905), Al Ain was lush with vegetation. Fruit trees were in abundance, wheat was grown and there was plenty of grass for the animals. In the mid-1900s, though, there was precious little of any vegetation aside from the palm groves. The people valued every bush and *ghaff* tree or *sumra* tree that was growing. But the only place to plant anything was in the date gardens which were watered by the *falaj* system. The *aflaaj,* built thousands of years ago, were the underground aqueducts which brought water from the Hajar mountains to the villages of Al Ain, and became the life-line of the oasis. The *falaj* provided water for the date, lime and mango trees and alfalfa and beans and also all the water for domestic needs as well as for their animals.

After a good rain, the desert would turn into a beautiful carpet of green, mingled with brown. The Arabs would greet each other with "*baraka*", meaning 'blessing'. Indeed, rain was a blessing to the thirsty desert sands and plains. Seeds that had lain dormant, sometimes for decades, sprung to life. They wiggled their fragile fresh green leaves and their delicate beautiful white or yellow flowers up towards the warm sun. Everyone was delighted to see them. Every bush would have little flowers as well, and the *ghaff* and the *sumra* trees seemed to get a new lease of life.

Some of the desert bushes were used for food, the fresh new tips chopped up and eaten with the staple rice and meat — an excellent source of vitamins and iron. The locals still like to eat the *arta* (a desert bush) whenever they can get it after a good rain. And even today, after a rain, families will all pile into their Landcruisers for picnics in the desert.

Plants that required little water, like the *habayya,* were seen near many of the homes. They provided a refreshing bit of greenery to the landscape with their Morning-glory type of flowers.

On one visit to Sheikh Shakhbut in the Abu Dhabi Hisn Palace, we found him and his men cutting up pods and picking out the seeds in order to plant trees in the grounds. He offered us

some too, which we gratefully received and planted at the hospital as well. These trees took very little water because of their extensive root system. They grew very fast and provided good shade.

But the camels also liked our trees. Night after night they would amble over to graze on our nice newly-sprouted trees. One night a staff member, tired not only of having the trees decimated but also his sleep wrecked by the noise of camels chomping, decided that he would take care of them. He got into the Land Rover and started to herd them away. Unfortunately in the excitement, one of the camels fell and broke its leg. This was double trouble. The owner of course was livid, eventually calming down only after the matter of compensation was settled.

IN THE EARLY 1960s, Sheikh Shakhbut had a pipeline built to take water from a good well in Saad, all the way to Abu Dhabi to provide sweet water for drinking and for plants. This line provided water for all of the outlying Bedouin encampments as well, and also water for all, on their long arduous trip to Abu Dhabi, be it by camel or Land Rover.

The artesian well at Ain Al Fayda was discovered in the late 1960s and was built up in 1971 as a resort area for Al Ain with hotel facilities and water canals leading to a big duck and swan reserve as well.

Today, there has been an almost unbelievable metamorphosis in the Oasis City. The beautiful parks and gardens, the tree-lined multi-laned avenues and the artistically-designed roundabouts all reveal a mastermind with vision and determination. Plans also call for Al Ain to have water from a desalination plant pumped in from Abu Dhabi. With more water available, agricultural production can be expanded.

AL AIN IS ALSO THE CENTRE for higher education, again fulfilling Sheikh Zayed's dream to make education available to all. He and his peers had not had that opportunity. Now his children and grandchildren can get the education they desire and deserve. Notable among the many facilities at Al Ain University is its agricultural programme with a Research Station set up to develop new and better varieties of produce. Chief beneficiaries of the research will be Al Ain and the whole of the UAE.

*The green and shady date palms
provided a welcome sanctuary.
Inset: The colourful parks of today.*

THE GOAT-SKIN BAGS that the Bedouin had hanging from the trees were used for their milk and water. The smaller bags — made from a mountain cat, or fox or *dhabb* (a lizard) — were used for butter or coffee beans or whatever small articles they needed to keep safe from sand and bugs.

A source of amazement was how the Bedouin could keep butter in the heat without refrigeration; it never tasted rancid. They would take the butter, which they made by rocking the milk back and forth in a goat-skin bag, add flour, salt, coriander and cumin, and then bring it to a boil. The flour would take the curds to the bottom of the pot and the resultant clarified liquid butter (*dihn*) would have a delightful flavour. It could be re-heated time after time to be put on their paper-thin bread (*khubz er raqaaq*), or on their rice, and still keep good.

Today the same kind of butter is used, only more of it and in everything — the *harees*, the *bellaleet*, the *khabees*, the *'aseed*, as well as on bread and rice.

The *dihn* was also used to make a date mixture, a staple for journeys such as the six-day camel trip from Al Ain to Abu Dhabi, or on the Haj. They would brown the flour in a pan over the fire, then add the butter and dates. The ingredients were heated until the dates were soft, then mixed together by hand. It would stay fresh even in the heat, and never go rancid. They would take out a bit at a time and re-heat it on the campfire. It was a nourishing, satisfying quick meal.

Camel's milk apparently doesn't have much butter-fat, so goat's milk would be used to make *dihn,* or preferably cow's milk. Goats were more readily available and easier to keep. In the early 1970s, some Holstein cattle were brought in from Holland, with Dutch cattlemen to take care of them. But the cattle adjusted very poorly to this climate, and didn't do too well. It has been suggested that they missed the classical music!

Above: Nurse Nancy Brock listens to a problem during a village visit, 1970. The woman's donkey is loaded with goatskins of water from the nearby village well.

Right: A young Omani with his goatskin water bags hanging from the wall, 1970.

IN 1964, WE WERE INVITED by Sheikh Zayed and the First Lady to join their group for a night on the dunes. But to get there we had to make the journey on camels provided by Sheikh Zayed. There were about ten or twelve of us. It took quite a while getting everyone loaded on the camels; we slid forward and then backwards, amid much squealing, as the camels laboriously stood up. The trip took about two to three hours but it seemed like a whole day. I have never been so thirsty in my life — or so sore in certain areas, from the unaccustomed jostling up and down, and the backwards and forwards rocking motion on the camel.

At the end of our camel ride, there was Sheikh Zayed waiting for us, having driven to the sand dunes of Masoudi. He enjoyed our antics in descending, exhausted, from the camels. They had ice water (there was an ice factory in Al Ain then) and several big juicy watermelons waiting for us. They tasted ever so good. Then they served us a supper on the dunes, the men on one dune and the women on the opposite one. After a lot of fun and talking, we hauled out our sleeping bags and chose a comfortable spot to sleep. In the morning we returned to Al Ain by car. Our host didn't insist that we ride the camels back. Maybe the camels wouldn't have relished another trip with such novices either.

THE ARABS WERE VERY ATTACHED to their camels. I remember seeing them disturbed, as we were, at the sound of a camel 'crying' when she had lost her newborn. It was pitiful. Another family handled the same situation by placing the stuffed skin of the dead baby beside the mother so that she could still smell her baby and be comforted. Such was their concern for their animals.

The camel, like the date palm, was the Arab's life. It provided them with transportation, milk and, ultimately, meat and also gave them a means of entertainment, in the camel races. Then as now, these were a time of special celebration and social gathering. Owners and spectators enjoyed driving beside the running camels in their Land Rovers to egg them on and to cash in on the excitement first-hand, rather than from the sidelines.

Top: Watering the camels, early 1970s.
Above: Traditional life in modern Al Ain.
Right: Aboard the regal-looking camel sits Issa bin Jabar, 1964. The boy in front had received treatment for a camel bite.

THE SERVING OF COFFEE is one of the unique rituals of Arab hospitality. When they travelled by camel, the coffee pot was the last thing to be packed and the first thing to be unpacked. Even today, the flask of coffee goes everywhere — even in a Range Rover on a short trip out to the desert, or a Mercedes on a trip to Abu Dhabi or Dubai.

The preparation of the coffee was as much a ritual as was the serving. They bought the raw green coffee beans, which were always roasted fresh each day, or for each brew, over an open fire. A heavy skillet was preferred to roast the coffee beans, but often the Bedouin used a tin with a heavy wire attached to it for a handle. Everyone roasted it to his own taste. Then the beans were crushed with a mortar and pestle, usually made of brass.

What followed was the most tantalising smell of freshly-brewed coffee. The coffee was brought to a boil in a large kettle over an open fire, just so that it would rise two or three times, and then it was poured into the brass coffee pot, the *della* (or flask nowadays) over the whole, pounded cardamom in the pot.

The pouring or serving of coffee itself is a real art. The coffee pot is held in the left hand, and the right hand holds five or six of the small handle-less cups called *finjaans*, clinking them together in a rhythmical fashion. The *della* is then raised up and poured, lowered over the *finjaan* as they are filled — for the men, about one-half full; for the women, about a third or even a quarter full.

Sometimes the coffee is very strong, and you're glad there is only a small amount. But you can have as many servings as you like (which is only a few sips, but always hot) if there are just a few of you. When you don't want any more, you just give the cup a gentle shake, and give it back to the server. If there is a room full of people, you will drink only one cup and that will then be refilled for the next one down the line all around the room.

The brass coffee pot was always kept on the edge of the fire to keep it hot. What a blessing the vacuum flask was, especially in the summer, so a fire no longer had to be kept burning; for the coffee, then, as now, must be ready to serve all day long.

Sheikh Tahnoun bin Mohammed Al Nahyan watches coffee being made in the traditional manner. The coffee beans are being roasted in a heavy skillet on an open fire.

Omani woman pounding her coffee, 1967. The pounding had a rhythm to it, with the pestle hitting the side of the container to give it a real ring. It was the most welcome sound while sitting out in the sand, or in an 'arish or a mud-block room, to hear the coffee being pounded.

MY COLLEAGUES AND I WERE PRIVILEGED to have had the opportunity of getting acquainted with members of the Ruling family. It is perhaps even a 'sacred trust', as privilege always carries with it responsibility. I consider it, then, a privilege to be able to pay a tribute to Sheikh Zayed's mother. She was precious to us, as she was to her family, extended family, and all who knew her.

Sheikha Salaama bint Butti Al Qubaisi, fondly known as *Umm esh Shyuukh* — the mother of the rulers — was no doubt one of the greatest women of this country. She was a Falaahi, a Qubaisi on her father's side and Al Sultan on her mother's side. Her father was Butti bin Khadem Al Qubaisi and her mother was Mouzi bint Haamid Al Sultan. She was born in about 1890 and died in 1970.

When I first met her, I was impressed with her regal bearing and her kindness even though I could not understand what she was saying, as I didn't know Arabic then. She was pleasant, happy and contented and known far and wide for her kindness and generosity. Women would come to her for advice in family matters and health problems. She was their judge, doctor and mother.

She controlled the household, not with an iron rod, but from a loving devotion. In her latter years, her daughter was always at her side tending to her needs and passing on instructions to the rest of the household. Her personal servant, Nimlu, was also dedicated to her, and at the time of her death, felt the loss as deeply as any family member.

Because her health was frail, Dr Marian Kennedy and the nurses were frequently called to her home to treat her. It was hard for the family to remember when to give her which pill, so we would go every day, often twice a day, to see that she was getting the medicines she needed. We would sort them out from the packages which were stored in a little tin beside her bed. She was always pleasant and grateful; and she became our teacher. She taught us many Arabic sayings which we have never forgotten.

In January of 1964, she came to the hospital for a prolonged stay. A lady doctor and her nurse were flown in from London to treat her. While the family members stayed in a tent, which they pitched beside the hospital, she stayed in our operating room, the biggest room that we had. But we had the privilege in those days of sitting with her there every day, probably three times a day.

The family did their cooking beside the tent; it was then that I was introduced to many local foods, and tried the *halwa* or sweetmeat. I learned about their perfumes (the heavy *'aoud, ambar, zafran,* musk, sandal, etc.) Sheikha Salaama would patiently correct our Arabic, but would also laugh with us at our mistakes. Even today when I use some of her phrases, Arab companions sit up and listen. "Where did you learn that?" they will ask. Some of them still recognise words and sayings as coming from Sheikha Salaama bint Butti.

Sheikh Zayed also came to see her nearly every day, so that was another privilege for us to be able to sit with him there, as we also did when she was at home. Sheikh Zayed's sister lived there at their home and his brothers and cousins would all come to visit frequently.

I PARTICULARLY REMEMBER one evening in 1970, when Sheikh Zayed and Sheikh Tahnoun were there together with Sheikh Shakhbut; they started singing their old Bedouin *qaseedas* or ballads. They thoroughly enjoyed them, as did also their mother, of course, especially as they were singing for her.

Sheikha Salaama raised and influenced the destiny of four sons, Shakhbut, Hazaa, Khalid and Zayed, and one daughter. Two of those sons, Shakhbut and Zayed, have ruled Abu Dhabi for close to 70 years. Her daughter married the late Sheikh Mohammed bin Khalifa bin Zayed.

Sheikha Salaama had an inherent gift of wisdom, and her sons would consult with her. It was because of her that the former ruler of Abu Dhabi, Sheikh Shakhbut, stayed in power for 38 years. She had made the brothers swear over her body (on their mother's milk) that they would protect him.

She was happy for Sheikh Zayed at his accession in 1966. In those early years of Sheikh Zayed's reign, he spent much of his time in Al Ain, and he faithfully visited his mother nearly every day. She looked forward to his visits to learn what was going on in the country, but more, just to enjoy his jovial conversation and laughter. He brought a ray of sunshine and cheer to her life.

When Sheikha Salaama passed away in October of 1970, the whole country felt the loss. It was the end of an era, of a great stateswoman.

Sheikh Zayed with three of his sons: Sheikh Mohammed (second from right), Sheikh Hamdan (third from right), and Sheikh Hazaa (right), about 1970.

View across Al Ain with the Hilton Hotel in the background, 1970.

ACKNOWLEDGEMENTS

WHEN I CAME TO AL AIN in 1962, I had borrowed my brother's camera so that I could send a few photos back to help family and friends picture where I was working. With them in mind, I went about photographing things which interested me, at random, never dreaming that one day the photos that my colleagues and I were taking would hold sufficient interest to be published.

Many people over the years have inspired me. I would like first to thank the people of the UAE for their friendship and their encouragement to write this book, and above all HH Sheikh Zayed bin Sultan Al Nahyan, President of the United Arab Emirates and Ruler of Abu Dhabi, whose abiding interest in his people's heritage is an example to all. Sheikh Zayed made it possible for us to be here and to enjoy the benefits that came with prosperity.

I want to thank all of my colleagues and friends for their help. I am especially grateful to those who sent pictures to be used, namely Doctors Pat and Marian Kennedy, Joyce Melhuish and Mona Joyce. Thank you for your invaluable contribution to what really is 'our' book; ours because each of you as well could have told this story, weaving in different incidents perhaps, but ultimately arriving at the same place. I hope my memory has served me well; I know you will forgive any oversights.

I would also like to express my gratitude to the staff of Motivate Publishing, especially my editor Chuck Grieve.

Finally, thanks to Mr Juma bin Ahmed Al Salami, of the Al Salami Group, without whose sponsorship support publication of this book would not have been possible.

AL SALAMI GROUP
AL AIN

THE ARABIAN HERITAGE SERIES

Arabian Profiles
edited by Ian Fairservice and Chuck Grieve

Land of the Emirates
by Shirley Kay

Enchanting Oman
by Shirley Kay

Bahrain – Island Heritage
by Shirley Kay

Kuwait – A New Beginning
by Gail Seery

Dubai – Gateway to the Gulf
edited by Ian Fairservice

Abu Dhabi – Garden City of the Gulf
by Peter Hellyer and Ian Fairservice

Sharjah – Heritage and Progress
by Shirley Kay

Fujairah – An Arabian Jewel
by Peter Hellyer

Portrait of Ras Al Khaimah
by Shirley Kay

Gulf Landscapes
by Elizabeth Collas and Andrew Taylor

Birds of Southern Arabia
by Dave Robinson and Adrian Chapman

Falconry and Birds of Prey in the Gulf
by Dr David Remple and Christian Gross

The Living Desert
by Marycke Jongbloed

The Living Seas
by Frances Dipper and Tony Woodward

Mammals of the Southern Gulf
by Christian Gross

Seafarers of the Gulf
by Shirley Kay

Architectural Heritage of the Gulf
by Shirley Kay and Dariush Zandi

Emirates Archaeological Heritage
by Shirley Kay

Sketchbook Arabia
by Margaret Henderson

Storm Command
by General Sir Peter de la Billière

Looking for Trouble
by General Sir Peter de la Billière

This Strange Eventful History
by Edward Henderson

Juha – Last of the Errant Knights
by Mustapha Kamal,
translated by Jack Briggs

Mother Without a Mask
by Patricia Holton

Zelzelah – A Woman Before Her Time
by Mariam Behnam

The Wink of the Mona Lisa
by Mohammad Al Murr,
translated by Jack Briggs

Fun in the Emirates
by Aisha Bowers and Leslie P Engelland

Fun in the Gulf
by Aisha Bowers and Leslie P Engelland

Premier Editions

A Day Above Oman
by John Nowell

A Day Above the Emirates
by John Nowell

Forts of Oman
by Walter Dinteman

Land of the Emirates
by Shirley Kay

Abu Dhabi – Garden City of the Gulf
edited by Ian Fairservice and Peter Hellyer

50 Great Curries of India
by Camellia Panjabi

The Thesiger Library

Written and photographed
by Wilfred Thesiger:

Arabian Sands
The Marsh Arabs
Desert, Marsh and Mountain
My Kenya Days
Visions of a Nomad

The Thesiger Collection
a catalogue of photographs
by Wilfred Thesiger

Thesiger's Return
by Peter Clark
with photographs by Wilfred Thesiger

Arabian Heritage Guides

**Off-Road in the Emirates
Volumes 1 & 2**
by Dariush Zandi

Off-Road in Oman
by Heiner Klein and Rebecca Brickson

Snorkelling and Diving in Oman
by Rod Salm and Robert Baldwin

The Green Guide to the Emirates
by Marycke Jongbloed

Beachcombers' Guide to the Gulf
by Tony Woodward

On Course in the Gulf
by Adrian Flaherty

Spoken Arabic – Step-by-Step
by John Kirkbright

Arabian Albums

Written and photographed
by Ronald Codrai:

Dubai – An Arabian Album
Abu Dhabi – An Arabian Album
**The North-East Shaikhdoms –
An Arabian Album**
Travels to Oman – An Arabian Album

MOTIVATE
PUBLISHING